Sea Of Feelings

Author & Illustrator: Farrah Raines

ISBN:978-1-7376934-0-6

To all my students past, present and future, for being the inspiration to write this book. I also dedicate this book to all my love ones who helped me when I was learning to swim in my own sea of feelings. My life would not be the same without all of you!!!

Hello, my name is Scuba Farrah. Today I am going on an underwater adventure to learn about feelings.

Scuba Farrah said, "I feel happy today which means my body is calm and my mind is ready to learn about different feelings."

"Starfish, you look happy!",
said Scuba Farrah.

"I am feeling happy and that
makes me want to smile!", said
Starfish.

"My body feels "just right" when I am happy. That means my body does not feel fast like a swimming Killer Whale, or slow like a Sea Slug", said Starfish.

"Look, I see a Jellyfish!", said Scuba Farrah.

"Jelly, I am learning about feelings. Can you tell me how you are feeling right now?", asked Scuba Farrah.

"I feel silly today!", said Jelly.

"Jelly, what does silly feel like to you?". asked Scuba Farrah.

"When I feel silly I laugh a lot!", said Jelly.

Jelly explained to Scuba Farrah, "Feeling silly makes my body move fast. That is why I wiggle my tentacles through the water making tons of bubbles."

"Feeling silly looks different for my friend Whale. Whale has a hard time focusing. This means trouble with ears listening, and eyes looking", said Jelly.

"Oh no, this part of the ocean is creepy looking. I feel scared seeing Tiger Sharks swimming through this old shipwreck", said Scuba Farrah nervously.

"Blow Fish, you look scared!", said Scuba Farrah.

Blow Fish quietly answered, "I am feeling scared with all the tiger sharks swimming around us."

"What does scared feel like to you?",
asked Scuba Farrah.

"Feeling scared makes my heart beat
super fast. Sometimes I have a hard
time breathing!", said Blow Fish.

"When I feel scared my body puffs up three times my original size. I gulp large amounts of water making my body bigger. Then I can't swim, I just drift along until my body returns to normal size", said Blow Fish.

Grabbing her head Scuba Farrah said, "Bad weather ruins my diving which makes me mad!"

"Crab, your face tells me you feel mad! What does mad feel like to you?", asked Scuba Farrah.

"I do feel mad! Feeling mad makes my claws start to snap all over making it hard to stop", said Crab.

18

"My body tightens, my heart speeds up, and my face gets hot when I feel mad", said Crab.

"Diving by myself gets lonely, and makes me feel sad", said Scuba Farrah.

Scuba Farrah asked, "Angelfish, what does sad feel like to you?"

Angelfish answered, "My mouth will form a frown, and sometimes I will cry when I feel sad."

"When I am sad my body slows down and I can't swim with the other fish. I also have a lot of trouble thinking of anything other than what made me sad.", said Angelfish.

"I feel sick, I need to take a break from diving. My head hurts, my stomach is churning, and my face is green", said Scuba Farrah.

Scuba Farrah said, "Look, I found a Seahorse laying down. His tail is anchored to seaweed so he does not float away while sleeping."

"Seahorse, how does sick feel to you?", asked Scuba Farrah

"Feeling sick makes me lose my appetite. I will pass on the Minnows and Shrimp today, my stomach feels tight like a knot. Being sick makes my body feel tired and slow", Seahorse said.

"All this diving made me hungry! I keep thinking about the food I packed for lunch", said Scuba Farrah.

Scuba Farrah asked, "Shark, what does hungry feel like to you?"

"Feeling hungry makes my stomach growl. I am a slow swimmer when I am hungry", said Shark.

"I learned a lot about different feelings today! My mind is feeling all jumbled up", said Scuba Farrah.

" I know what you mean Scuba Farrah. After all this talk about different feelings my head feels dizzy!", said Octopus.

"Scuba Farrah, I am experiencing more than one feeling. I feel happy to see you, but I also feel tired from this big adventure", said Octopus.

Scuba Farrah said, "Yes, Octopus its time to end this adventure about feelings today."

"Thank you friends I learned so much about feelings, and how they effect everyone differently. I hope you did too!", said Scuba Farrah.

THE END

Feeling Activities

1. Read the book and discuss each sea creature feelings. Make a chart and use emoji stickers to check in on how your child feels daily.

2. Act out each feeling during the story, or play feeling charades.

3. Draw your favorite character from the story. Talk about the drawing and how they feel.

4. Listen to music that reflects different feelings. (For example slow music to represent feeling sad, and fast music to represent feeling silly.)

5. Make faces in front of a mirror. This is a great way for the child to see their own expressions paired with talking about feelings.

ABOUT THE AUTHOR

Author and Illustrator Farrah Raines has 17 years experience of working with children as an pediatric occupational therapy assistant. Her background expands to a license massage therapist, children's yoga and mindfulness instructor, color guard instructor, blogger, and public speaker. Farrah is very passionate about working with children to provide sensory tools to assist with self regulation skills. She also enjoys reaching out to families to provide resources and training's to help support their child.

Check out her Miss Farrah's Movement and Fun YouTube Channel and website www.missfarrahmovementandfun.com for more children themed activities, and parent resources.

Made in United States
Orlando, FL
26 October 2023

38267624R00022